BRUCE COCHRAN

BRUCE COCHRAN

Cheep Thrills

NORTHWORD
PRESS INC.
MINOCQUA, WI 54548

© Bruce Cochran, 1994

Cover Design by Wayne Parmley
Other Design by Amy Monday

Published by
NorthWord Press, Inc.
P.O. Box 1360
Minocqua, WI 54548

For a free catalog describing NorthWord's line of books and gift items, call toll free 1-800-336-5666.

Printed in the United States of America

ISBN 1-55971-437-9

Library of Congress Cataloging-in-Publication Data

Cochran, Bruce
      Cheep thrills / by Bruce Cochran.
           p. cm.
      ISBN 1-55971-437-9
      1. Bird watching--Caricatures and cartoons. 2. American wit and humor, Pictorial.
      I. Title.
   NC1429. C619A4 1994
   741.5'973--dc20   94-19302
                                                  CIP

BEGINNING BIRD WATCHING

"HI! MY NAME IS KIMBERLY.
I'LL BE YOUR WAITRESS TODAY."

"IT LOOKS LIKE A ROBIN...ONLY BIGGER."

"CHEEP!"

"THE BOOK SAYS THEY'LL FIGHT FIERCELY TO PROTECT THEIR NEST."

"FIRST ROBIN OF SPRING, HUH?
WELL, BEAT IT. IT'S ONLY FEBRUARY."

"PROBABLY SOME SORT OF MATING RITUAL."

"THEY'RE CELEBRATING THE FIRST DAY OF SPRING."

"HOW DO YOU SUPPOSE THEY FIND THEIR WAY BACK TO THE SAME HOUSE EVERY YEAR?"

"I THOUGHT THEY JUST SANG TO ATTRACT A MATE."

"IT MUST BE SPRING. I HEARD A ROBIN COUGH."

15

"ITS SONG IS A THUNDERING 'CHUNGA-BOINGA, CHUNGA-BOINGA, CHUNGA-BOINGA' FOLLOWED BY LOUD SWEARING."

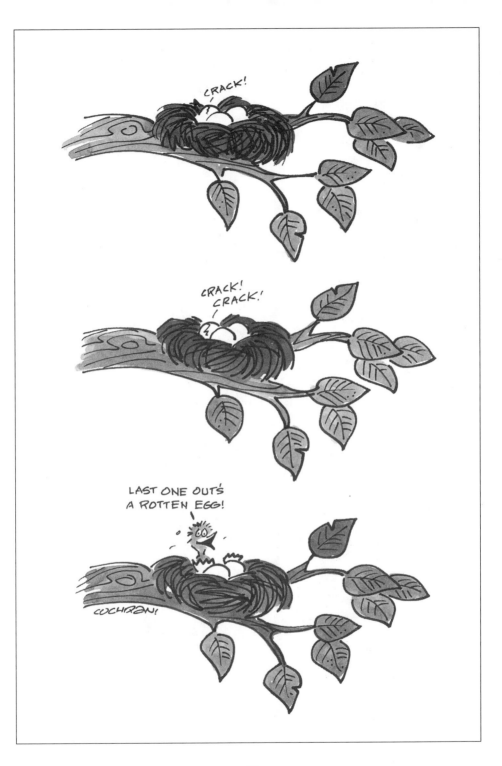

"WATCH THIS."

"WHO HAD THE CHEESEBURGER WITH NO ONIONS?"

"I THINK OF IT AS SORT OF A MOBILE HOME."

"I'LL BET YOU HAD NO IDEA IT WOULD TURN OUT LIKE THIS WHEN YOU PICKED ME UP AT THAT BIRD FEEDER LAST WINTER."

"HOW'S EVERYTHING AT THE TOP OF THE FOODCHAIN?"

"THE DOCTOR THINKS IT'S QUINTUPLETS."

"WHERE'D HE GO? HE WAS THERE JUST A SECOND AGO!"

"WE HAD MOUSE FOR BREAKFAST AND SNAKE FOR LUNCH. WHAT SOUNDS GOOD FOR DINNER?"

"I'M NOT A WHOOPER. I'M A **WHOPPER.**"

"I ASKED MYSELF, 'IF I WAS A BIRD, WHAT WOULD I WANT?'"

"I UNDERSTAND WE'RE GOING CONDO."

"TIME FOR THE CHRISTMAS BIRD COUNT AGAIN ALREADY?"

"HERE COMES OLD BIRD LEGS."

"YOU'RE LOST, AREN'T YOU?"

"EVERYWHERE YOU GO NOWADAYS SOMEONE'S TRYING
TO SELL YOU SOMETHING."

"YOU GONNA EAT THAT WORM?"

"I TOLD YOU WE SHOULDN'T MIGRATE DURING THE RUSH HOUR, BUT NOOOOO. YOU WOULDN'T LISTEN..."

"I'VE HEARD OF MOULTING, BUT THIS IS RIDICULOUS!"

"ACCORDING TO THIS BOOK YOU SHOULD HAVE BEEN IN SOUTH AMERICA TWO WEEKS AGO!"

"QUICK, MARGARET! f 5.6 AT 500!"

"COME AND GET IT!"

"TIPTONVILLE? ABOUT FIVE MILES THAT'A WAY, AS THE CROW FLIES."

"IT MAY BE BIRD FOOD TO THEM BUT IT'S BAIT TO ME."

"THE EVERGLADES? 700 MILES THAT WAY, THEN TURN LEFT. YOU CAN'T MISS THEM."

"WHAT DID YOU EXPECT? IT'S SATURDAY NIGHT."

"ACTUALLY I'M NOT AN ORDINARY CONDOR.
I'M A TIME-SHARING CONDOR."

"I'M TRYING TO FIND MYSELF."

"YOU MUST HAVE A VERY LARGE BIRD."

"MUST BE A CATBIRD."

"IT'S A LOT OF TROUBLE TO FILL BUT I ONLY HAVE TO DO IT
ONCE A YEAR."

"DON'T TRY TO BE A HERO, MARVIN! GIVE HIM
THE SUNFLOWER SEEDS!"

"WHAT ARE YOU IN FOR?"

"ANOTHER ATMOSPHERIC INVERSION, HUH?"

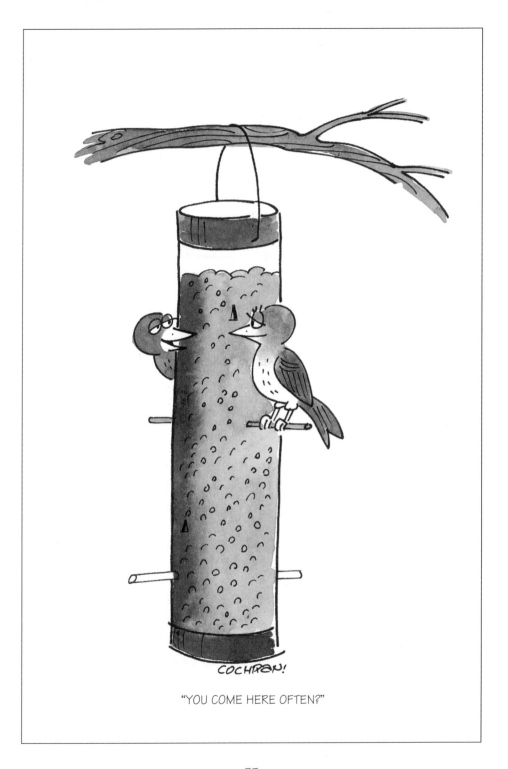

"YOU COME HERE OFTEN?"

"WHEN WE FIND IT, I HOPE IT'S IN A GOOD MOOD."

"WE'RE WARBLERS SON. WE DON'T **TWITTER**."

"YOU ACTUALLY BELIEVE THAT 'EARLY BIRD GETS THE WORM' CRAP, DON'T YOU?"

"DON'T EAT THE SUNFLOWER SEEDS. THEY GIVE YOU GAS."

"AND WE ALWAYS THOUGHT THEY WERE SO APPRECIATIVE."

"I'VE BEEN WORKING OUT."

"... SO ONE DAY I DECIDED, 'WHY BE CONTENT WITH JUST **WATCHING** THEM?'"

"TOOK TEN MINUTES TO PULL HIM OUT! WEIGHED ALMOST A QUARTER OF AN OUNCE!..."

"IT'S NOT MY NATURAL HABITAT BUT SO WHAT, IT'S COMFORTABLE."

"I GOT THEM 'BIRD OF DISTINCTION, BUT OH-SO-NEAR EXTINCTION BLUES'...
OH MY....YES I DO...."

"RURAL, SCHMURAL, I LIKE A LITTLE EXCITEMENT IN MY LIFE."

"WELL, YOU'LL JUST HAVE TO HOLD IT TIL WE GET TO THE NEXT STATUE."

"HELLO! BIRD IDENTIFICATION HOT LINE?..."

"YOU'RE GROWING UP, SON. IT'S TIME I TOLD YOU ABOUT THE PEOPLE AND THE BEES."

"NOT ONLY DID I GET THE PIGEON'S PEANUTS, I REALLY SCARED A COUPLE LITTLE OLD LADIES."

"CHIRPING OR NON-CHIRPING?"

"THEY WANT YOU TO FILL THE FEEDERS."

"COME ON, HONEY! WE'RE ALONE; HOW ABOUT A LITTLE SMOOCH?
WHO'S GONNA SEE US?"

"JUST BE GLAD *YOUR* BREEDING HABITS AREN'T DESCRIBED IN A BOOK!"

"BLUEBIRD OF HAPPINESS? NO WAY! I'M THE 'GRACKLE OF GRUMPINESS.'
NOW GET OUT OF THAT BED!"

"HARRY'S NOT VERY SEXY BUT HE'S A GREAT PROVIDER."

"I **TOLD** YOU THE PARK WASN'T SAFE ANYMORE!"

"O.K., YOU CAN HAVE THE DECK! JUST LEAVE US THE APARTMENT!"

"HOW WISE CAN HE BE? HE SLEEPS ALL DAY, THEN LOOKS FOR FOOD IN THE DARK."

"NEEDS A LITTLE MORE BURNT UMBER ON THE SCAPULARS."

"IT LOOKS LIKE A PURPLE SHOULDERED SAP SUCKER BUT ITS SHOULDERS AREN'T PURPLE AND IT ISN'T SUCKING SAP."

"SPAGHETTI?! OOOOH, **GROSS**! YOU'RE KIDDING! SAY IT'S A WORM!
PU-LEEZE!!"

"DON'T HORSE HIM IN! KEEP YOUR FEET PLANTED! DON'T GIVE
HIM ANY SLACK!"

"MOM, LEROY CALLED ME 'BIRD BRAIN'!"

"SQUIRREL PROOF. **HA!**"

"IT'S A BIRD FOOD PIZZA."

"NO JACUZZI?"

"YOU NEVER KNEW YOUR UNCLE MARVIN. HE WAS SUCKED INTO THE STARBOARD ENGINE OF A 727 OVER LOS ANGELES INTERNATIONAL IN '92."

"KEEP AN EYE ON IT WHILE I GO CALL THE AUDUBON SOCIETY."

"HECK NO, I DON'T WANT ANY ENCYCLOPEDIAS! NOW BEAT IT!"

"ITS SONG IS A HIGH-PITCHED 'HOO-WEEE, HOOO-WEEE. IT DOESN'T SAY ANYTHING ABOUT A DANCE."

"GESUNDHEIT."

"WHEN DID YOU FIRST NOTICE THIS FEAR OF FLYING?"

"I KNEW HE WAS GETTING TOO BIG AND STRONG FOR THE CAGE WHEN HE WANTED A TIRE INSTEAD OF A LITTLE SWING."

"PUT **THAT** ON YOUR LIFE LIST."

ABOUT BRUCE COCHRAN

Cartoonist Bruce Cochran brings his humor to us from a broad background in the outdoors as well as the arts.

Graduating from Oklahoma University with his Bachelor's in Design, he worked for Hallmark Cards as a writer/illustrator, and soon moved on to freelancing jobs with such publications as *Playboy, Look, Saturday Evening Post, Sports Afield, Field & Stream* and the nation's #1 selling newspaper, *USA Today.* His previous cartoon collections include *Buck Fever, Bass Fever* and *Duck Fever.*

His interest in the outdoors has made Cochran an avid hunter, fisherman, and collector of antique duck decoys. A sponsor member of Ducks Unlimited, his watercolors have been exhibited at the Easton Maryland Waterfowl Festival and the National Ducks Unlimited Wildlife Art Show, among others.